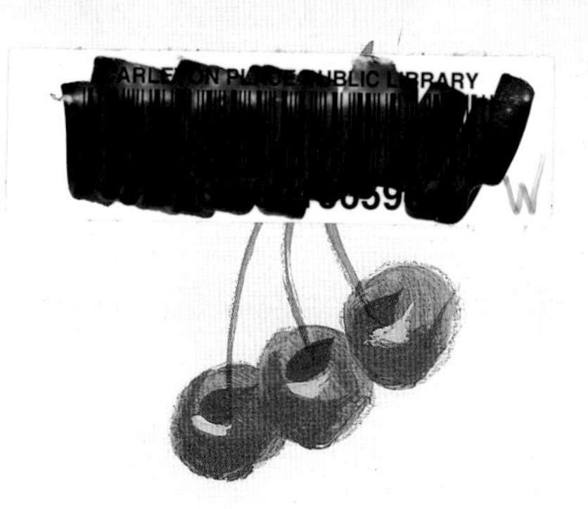
CARLETON PLACE PUBLIC LIBRARY

W9-BUX-380

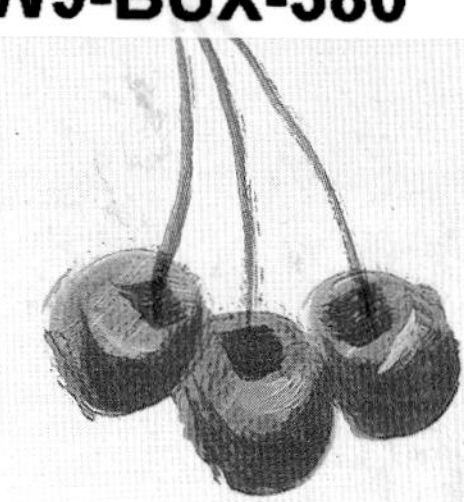

CARLETON PLACE
PUBLIC LIBRARY

For Phil and our children, Sean, Bethany, Joey and Katy. Love you all x.
And for Celia, my agent ~ with thanks ~ S W

For Faye, who is simply amazing! ~ C P

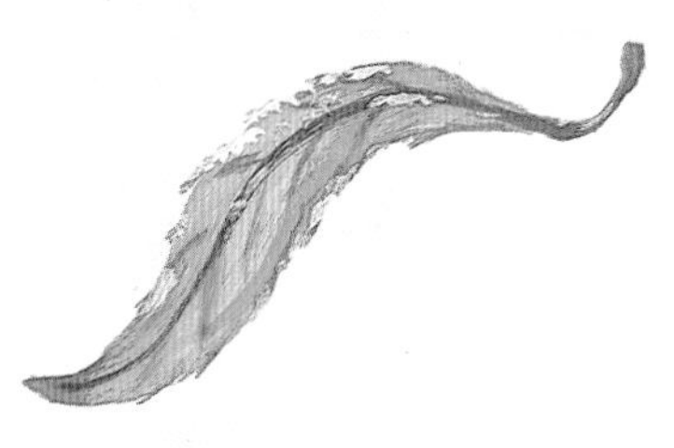

LITTLE TIGER PRESS
An imprint of Magi Publications
1 The Coda Centre
189 Munster Road, London SW6 6AW
www.littletigerpress.com

First published in Great Britain 2010

A CIP catalogue record for this book
is available from the British Library

ISBN 978-1-84895-093-1
Printed in China
LTP/1800/0043/0510
10 9 8 7 6 5 4 3 2 1

Noodle's Knitting

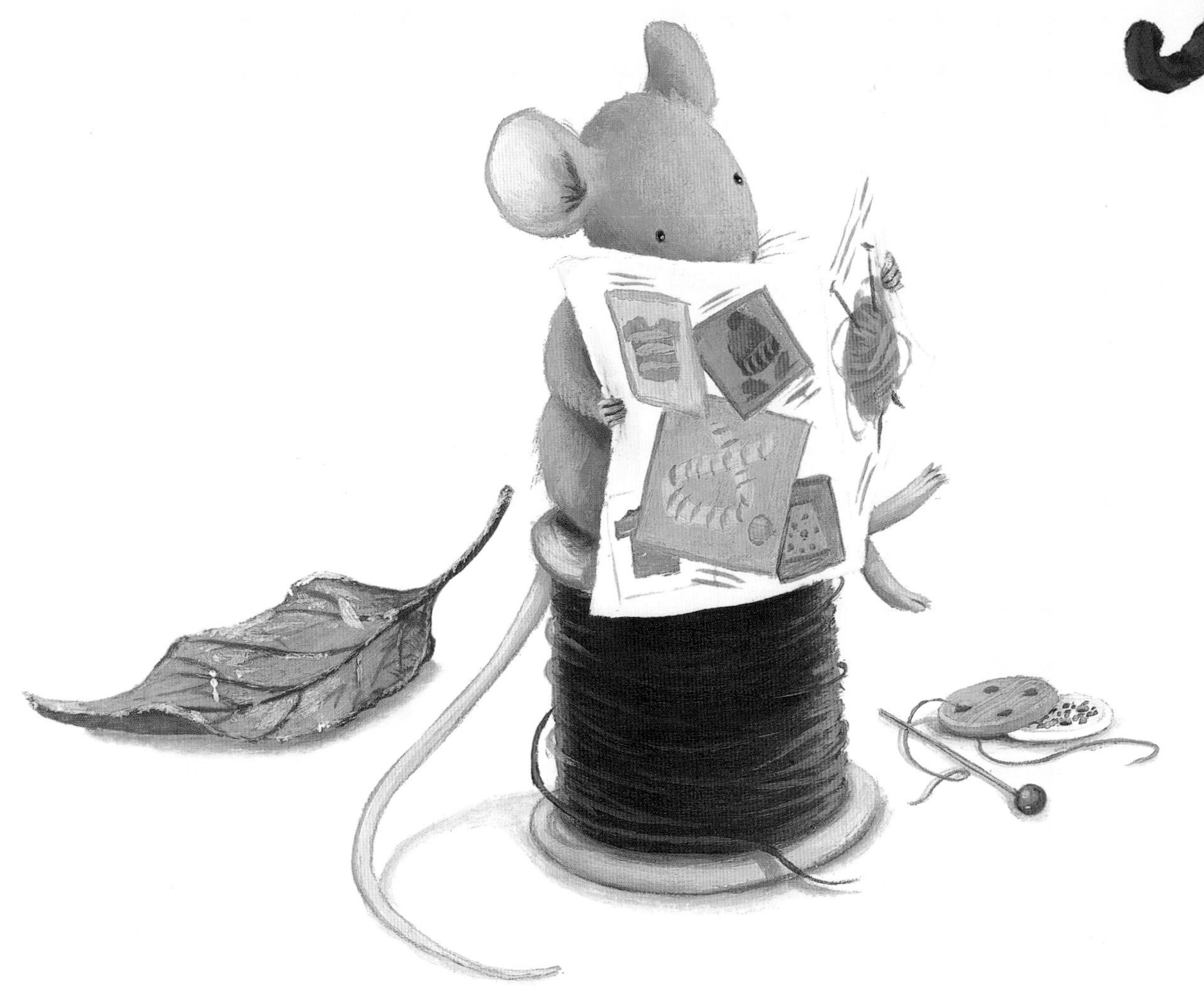

Sheryl Webster Caroline Pedler

LITTLE TIGER PRESS
London

Noodle hugged the snuggly wool tight.

She had always longed to knit. For months she had watched the farmer's wife knitting and whispered along to the special words:

"Knit one, purl one, knit two together!"

But today, suddenly the farmer's wife had cried, "It's quite the wrong colour!" and tossed her ball of wool aside. And now it was Noodle's!

"Just wait until the others see this!" she squeaked.

Panting, Noodle reached Hetty's house.

"Ooooh, there's a right chill in the air," Hetty grumbled. "My snout is quite blue! What have you got there, Noodle?"

"It's wool! I've got some wool," Noodle laughed. "Now all I need are knitting needles."

"Oh . . . I can help you there,"
snuffled Hetty. "Two of my prickles
should do just the job!"

"Wow! Thanks, Hetty!" gasped Noodle.
"Now I can start my super-snuggly scarf!"
And she set off home.

Noodle didn't get far before she just *had* to give it a try. She unravelled and threw . . .

and flicked . . .

and looped . . .

and . . .

oh dear!

"Silly me, I forgot to say the special words!" Noodle giggled.

"Knit one, purl one, knit two together!" she sang out.

As the needles looped the wool
a small row of stitches appeared.
"Ooh look what I did . . . look what
I did!" squeaked Noodle.

She hoppity skipped across the stepping stones . . .
"Knit one, slip one, knit two together," she sang. "Knit one . . .

forgetting all about
the wibbly wobbly one in the middle . . .
slipppppp!"

Luckily Bulgy popped up – just in time. "Careful, Noodle," he croaked. "It's a bit chilly for you to take a dip!"

"I *know*," twitched Noodle. "*Imagine* how wet my wool would have got! Thanks, Bulgy!" Then off she scurried.

Pitter patter went her paws, clickety click went her needles. On and on she danced, singing merrily,

"One plain, one purl, one twisk, one twirl!"

She was enjoying herself so much she didn't even notice her knitting catch on a prickle . . .

. . . or how it stretched
and streeeetched . . .

and streeeeeetched until...

. . . BOING!

Noodle flew back through the air!

"Noodle . . .
you're flying!" shouted a horrified Rosie. "Don't worry, I'll catch you!"

"Got you!" panted Rosie.

"Thank goodness my knitting's safe!" gasped Noodle. "Thank you, Rosie!"

And with a flickety flick of wool and
a clickety click of needles, Noodle
scampered into her little house.

Noodle yawned – but was much too excited to sleep. There was so much wonderful wool still to knit. And knit she did – all night long.

And as the ball of wool got smaller her knitting got longer...

and longer...

and longer!

"Yippee! It's finished!" Noodle squeaked at last. "Just wait until the others see this!"

But Noodle couldn't get to the door...

Her super-snuggly scarf was *everywhere*!
"Oh no . . . I'm knitted in!" squeaked Noodle.
Just then Noodle heard a tapping.

"Yoo-hoo, Noodle," called out Bulgy.
The three friends peeped and pointed and gasped!

"Oh Noodle," giggled Hetty.
"You have got in a pickle!"
"Don't worry – we'll soon have you out!"
twitched Rosie.

They all took hold of the knitting – and pulled!
And as they tugged and looped,
Noodle spun and swirled . . .
and whooped
and whirled!

"Oh . . . thank you!" she spluttered at last.
Noodle looked at her enormous scarf
and felt a little silly. "Whatever will
I do with all this?" she sighed.

"Do you know, Noodle – this is just *perfect*!" Hetty snuffled.

"You've made the most wonderful winter's nest ever," sighed Rosie.

"So I have!" Noodle squeaked happily. "And the best thing is . . .

"... it's big enough for us *all*!"

And as the snowflakes fell, the friends cosily huddled up together in their **super-snuggly scarf** for four!

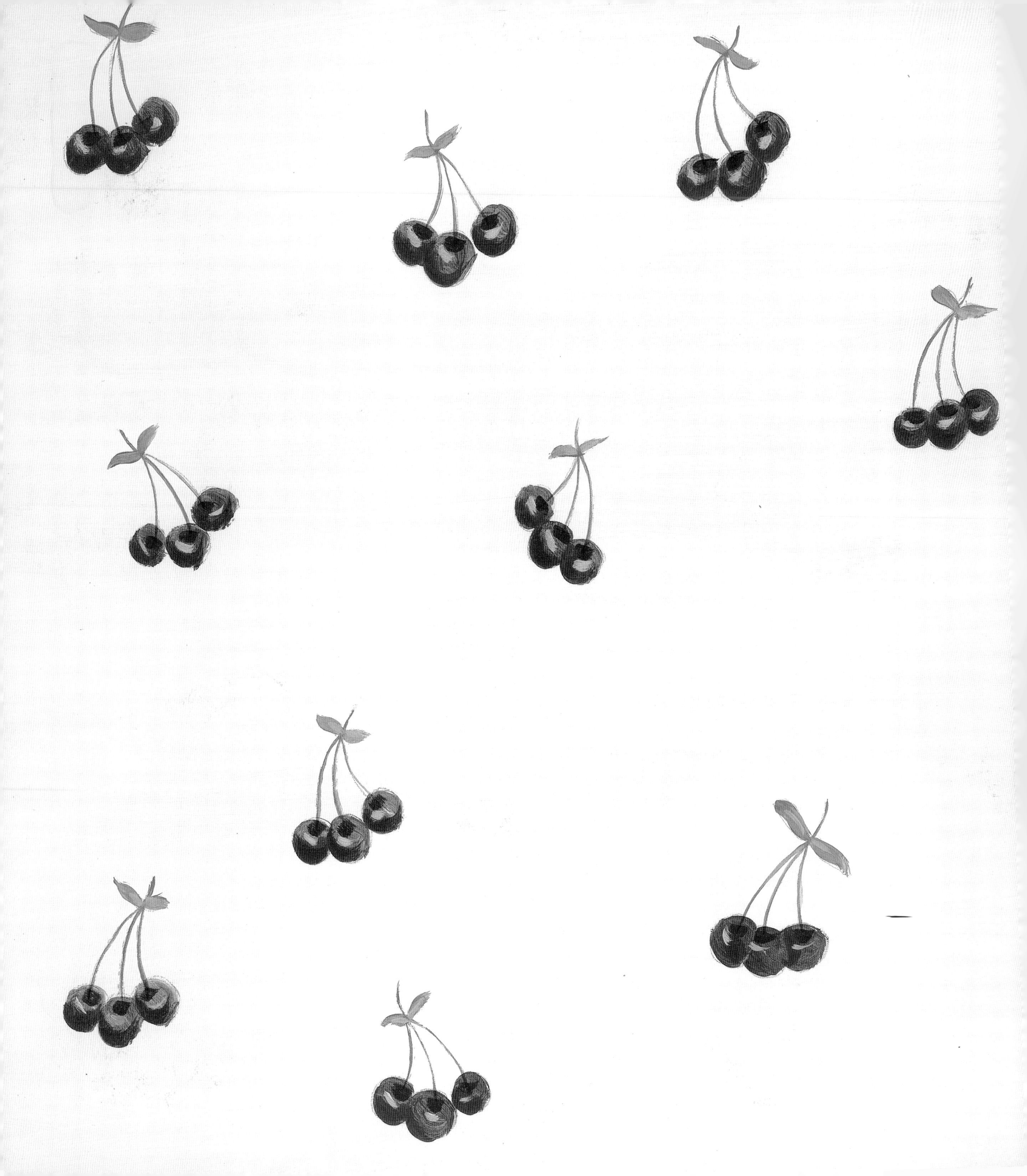